The Wild Ducks and the Goose

The Wild Ducks and the Goose

adapted by Carl Withers

drawings by Alan E. Cober

Holt, Rinehart and Winston   New York   Chicago   San Francisco

J
W

Books for young readers
by Carl Withers

The Wild Ducks and the Goose
The Tale of a Black Cat
I Saw a Rocket Walk a Mile
A Rocket in My Pocket

64883

There was once an old man
who lived with his wife in a
little round house, like this.

The house had a little round window, right here.

In front of the house
there was a nice big yard
with a long fence around it, like this.

And a long path led
from the front door
through the middle of the yard
down to the front gate, like this.

Not far away
was a pond, like this.

There was an island
in the pond, like this.

And there were fish
swimming round

in the water
of the pond,
like this.

Wild ducks also
used to come to the pond

and alight
on the island,
like this.

Two Indians came and
built their wigwams
near the pond so they
could hunt and fish there.

Here are the wigwams.

Early one morning the old man heard a great sound of QUACK, QUACKING in the sky. He looked out through the window and saw a flock of wild ducks, which flew down and alighted.

The man said to his wife, "There are wild ducks on the pond, and we are going to have some of those ducks for dinner."

The wife said, "You had better hurry up, or the Indians will get them first."

So he grabbed his gun
down off the wall and ran out
his back door and ran down
to the pond, like this.

As quickly as he could get to the edge of the pond he lifted his gun and fired it just as fast as he could, BANG! BANG! He fired both barrels, but his aim was not good, and all the ducks flew away from the other end of the pond, like this.

His shots woke up the two Indians, who got up quickly and ran out of their wigwams and down to the pond to see what had happened.

One Indian ran down to
the pond by this path.

And the other Indian ran down
to the pond by this path.

When they saw that the ducks were gone the Indians laughed because the man was such a poor shot.

The old man said nothing, but walked a little way along the edge of the pond to see if the ducks were going to fly back.

At last he put his gun
on his shoulder and
walked slowly back
to the house,

like this.

When he got inside the house his wife asked him, "Where are your ducks?"

He hung his gun back on the wall and said, "Well, well, I certainly made a goose of myself that time!"

AND HERE IS THE GOOSE!

About the Story

The Wild Ducks and The Goose is a drawing story based on two versions of a folktale that has been reported from places as far apart as Wisconsin and Denmark. The known versions of the present story differ somewhat in plot and picture, but all tell of a man living in a round house near a pond and all end up with a picture of a bird, not always a goose. A *drawing story* is one which the narrator illustrates as he tells. On blackboard or paper he creates the picture line by line as he tells the story. The picture is always a simple one that anybody, child or grownup, can draw, and the story always has a surprise ending.

Our story follows with several additions one with the same name in Clifton Johnson's *The Birch-Tree Fairy Book* (Little, Brown and Company, Boston, 1906). Where Clifton Johnson got the story is not known. He was both a remarkable collector of folktales and folk beliefs* and a skilled reteller of stories. He may have heard the story in his native Massachusetts or he may have based his telling on two fragmentary versions in *The Journal of American Folklore* (X, 1897: 323, and XI, 1898: 76). In the first, Ida C. Braddock recounts and pictures a tale, dimly recalled from her childhood, of an old man living by a pond. When two hunters pitched their tents nearby and "captured or slew a wild-fowl," the old man let the water out of the pond "to prevent their future exploits." In the second a contributer, A.B., summarizes a plot much like Johnson's. The story, he says, was his "earliest slate exercise in a country school nearly fifty years ago [i.e., about 1850] . . . taught him by an older pupil."

---

* His *What They Say in New England* (Lee and Shepard, Boston, 1896, reprinted with additional materials and an Introduction by Carl Withers, Columbia University Press, New York, 1963), was the first major collection of Anglo-American folktales and superstitions.

I have enlarged Johnson's story by adding the hunter's wife, the island, the fish, and the Indians and their wigwams. The picture has been amplified to include these details, which came from a story only partially remembered, from her Wisconsin childhood, by my friend Mrs. Adelin Linton, of New Haven, Conn., to whom grateful acknowledgment is given.

From far away Denmark comes a quite different version of the folktale, in which the bird is a stork. "When I was a child," writes Isak Dinesen in *Out of Africa* (Random House, New York, 1938, 251-52), "I was shown a picture—a kind of moving picture inasmuch as it was created before your eyes and while the artist was telling the story of it. The story was told, every time, in the same words." The man in her story lived in a round house with a long, *triangular* garden (the stork's long, pointed beak) near a pond with fish. One night a great noise wakened him. He ran hither and yon in the dark, falling twice (feet, legs, and knee joints come from the running and falling). He found the dam broken and the fish running out (tail). He mended the dam, went back to bed, looked out his window next morning, and—"What did he see?—A stork!"

Still another drawing story of a bird (unnamed) is told delightfully in Laura Ingalls Wilder's *On the Banks of Plum Creek* (Harper and Brothers, New York, 1937, 222-23). Here the bird's feet are homesteaders' tents and the tail is formed by fish flying out of the pond.

How many other versions of our drawing story are known? And how many other and different drawing stories are being told today? It would be wonderful to know.

CARL WITHERS

About the author: Carl Withers, noted anthropologist and folklorist, is the author of the much-loved *I Saw a Rocket Walk a Mile: Nonsense Tales, Chants and Songs from Many Lands, A Rocket in My Pocket: The Rhymes and Chants of Young Americans*, and *The Tale of a Black Cat*, another drawing story, as well as several other books for young people. Mr. Withers' interest in world-wide folklore has kept him researching and writing in this field for over twenty-five years. The drawing tale here is a "by-product" of that research. Mr. Withers was born in Missouri, attended Harvard College and Columbia University, and is now a resident of New York City.

About the artist: Named by the Artists' Guild as 1965 Artist of the Year, Alan E. Cober is primarily known for his work in the fields of magazine and advertising illustration. Recently, however, he has taken an interest in the illustration of children's books and illustrated *The Tale of a Black Cat*. His work for *The White Twilight* by Madeleine Polland and for *Smudge of the Fells* by Joyce Gard was honored by the Society of Illustrators. Mr. Cober studied at the University of Vermont and the School of Visual Arts. He and his wife, Ellen, and their two young children live in Ossining, New York, in their 160-year-old home.

About the book: Title is set in Pisa; the text is set in News Gothic Bold. The book was printed by offset. The illustrations were executed by Japanese bamboo pen and ink on soft paper.